Family

cowboy boot

alarm clock

Grandma Thora

stuffed bunny

suspenders

lollipop

handkerchief

footstool

Grandpa Dave

doll carriage

pudding

toothpaste

rubber duckie

baby bottle

D.W.

toothbrush

Baby Kate

pacifier

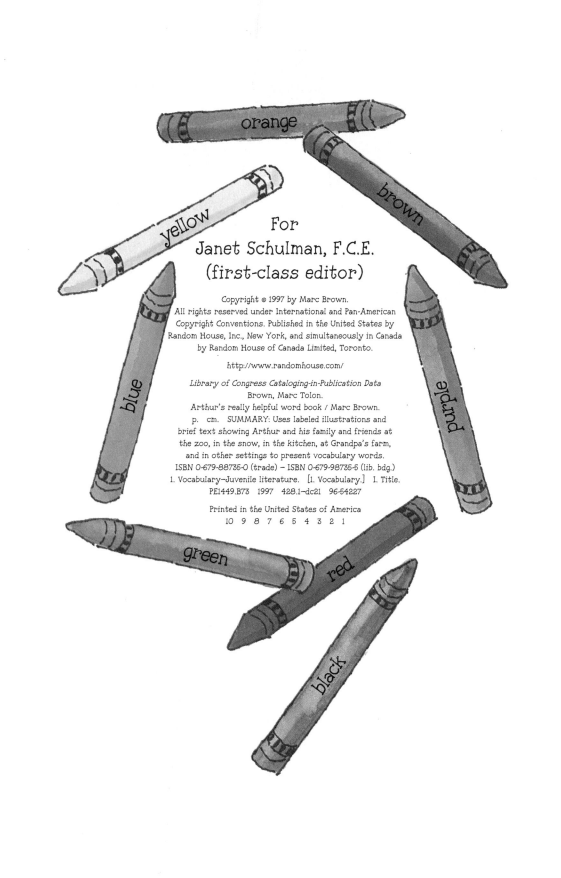

For
Janet Schulman, F.C.E.
(first-class editor)

http://www.randomhouse.com/

Library of Congress Cataloging-in-Publication Data
Brown, Marc Tolon.
Arthur's really helpful word book / Marc Brown.
p. cm. SUMMARY: Uses labeled illustrations and
brief text showing Arthur and his family and friends at
the zoo, in the snow, in the kitchen, at Grandpa's farm,
and in other settings to present vocabulary words.
ISBN 0-679-88735-0 (trade) – ISBN 0-679-98735-5 (lib. bdg.)
1. Vocabulary–Juvenile literature. [1. Vocabulary.] 1. Title.
PE1449.B73 1997 428.1–dc21 96-54227

Printed in the United States of America
10 9 8 7 6 5 4 3 2 1

scissors

hairbrush

lizard

pen

T-shirt

belt

birthday cake

party hat

slippers

pajamas

baby powder

telephone

spaghetti

ARTHUR'S REALLY HELPFUL
Word Book
MARC BROWN

anchor

drum

recorder

undershirt

balloon

Random House New York

beads

present

fireplace

roof

shutters

highchair

soap dish

shower curtain

towel

mirror

shampoo

faucet

toilet

paintbrush

door

sink

tub

At Arthur's House

Saturday is clean-up day and everyone is busy. What are some of the things you can do to help around your house?

awning

staircase

piano

chair

telephone

chest

table

light switch

circuit breaker

steps

tools

dirty clothes

vise

workbench

oil can

hot water heater

paint cans

light bulb

matches

iron

needle & thread

ironing board

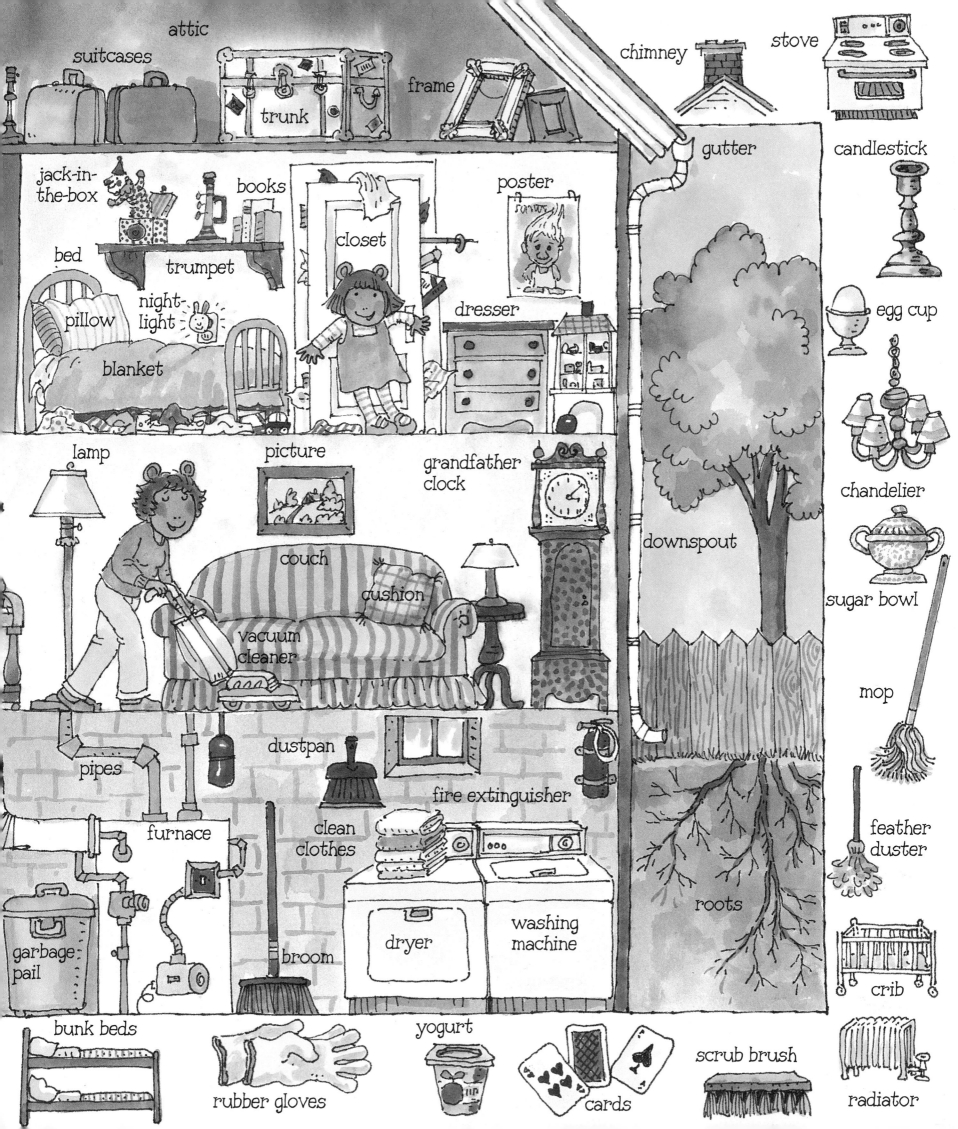

attic

suitcases

trunk

frame

chimney

stove

gutter

candlestick

jack-in-the-box

books

poster

egg cup

bed

closet

trumpet

dresser

chandelier

pillow

night-light

blanket

downspout

sugar bowl

lamp

picture

grandfather clock

mop

couch

cushion

vacuum cleaner

feather duster

dustpan

pipes

fire extinguisher

furnace

clean clothes

roots

crib

garbage pail

broom

dryer

washing machine

bunk beds

rubber gloves

yogurt

cards

scrub brush

radiator

deer

shark

elephant

crocodile

lion

giraffe

ostrich

panda

At the Zoo

Watching the sea lions is always fun, but today there is some real monkey business going on at the zoo. All of the monkeys have escaped. Can you help the zookeeper find them?

zebra

ticket booth

turnstile

zookeeper

bird

stroller

camel

dolphin

tiger

penguin

buffalo

leopard

hippopotamus

snake

parrots

hoop

fish

bucket

cardinal

ball

sea lion

turtle

balloons

gorilla

ICE CREAM

dog

anteater

polar bear

fox

peacock

At School with D.W.

Everyone is very busy at school today, including the class gerbil. He likes stories too!

Counting

From 1 to 10 – can you count these city things?

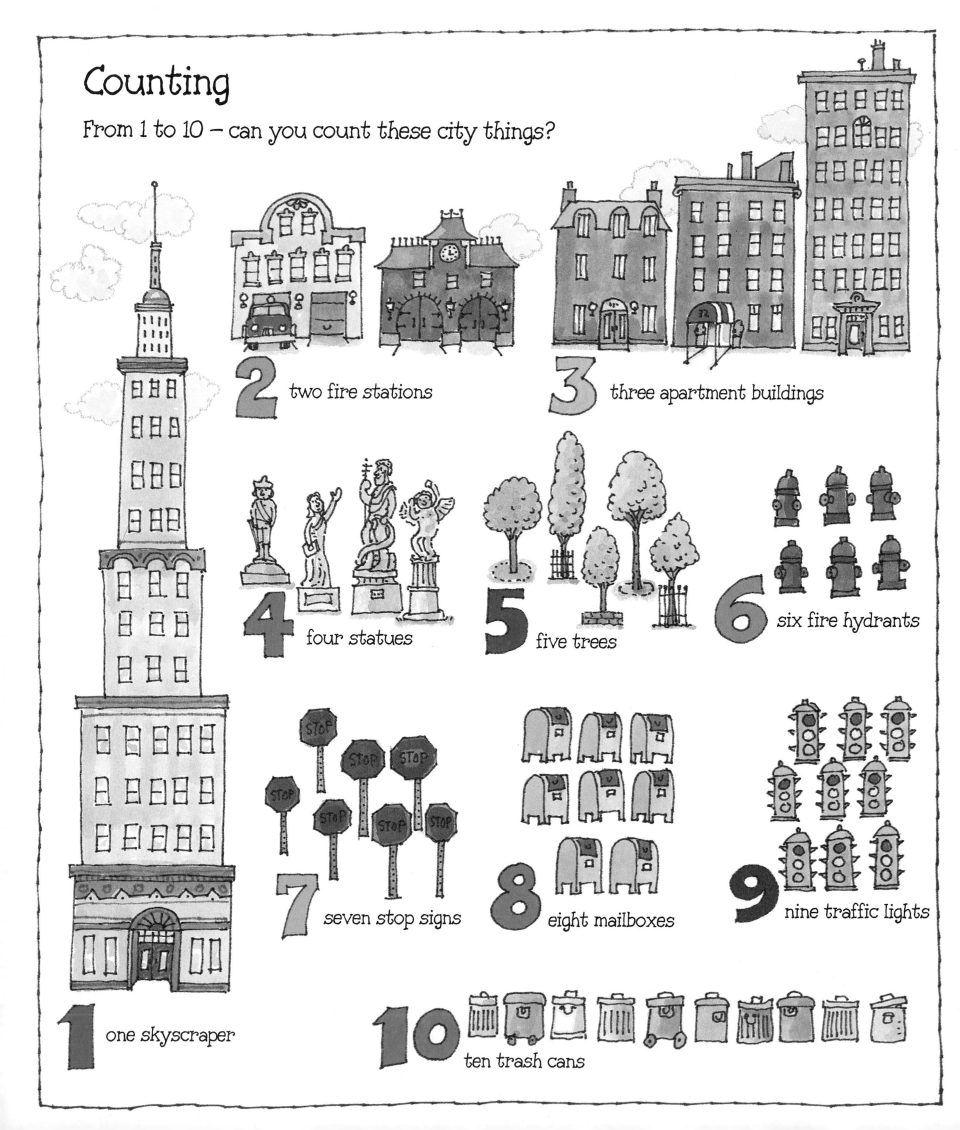

2 two fire stations

3 three apartment buildings

4 four statues

5 five trees

6 six fire hydrants

7 seven stop signs

8 eight mailboxes

9 nine traffic lights

1 one skyscraper

10 ten trash cans

Opposites

Do you know any others? Yes? No?

up   down   hot   cold   over   under

full   empty   asleep   awake   high   low

slow   fast   happy   sad   on   off

big   little   sweet   sour   young   old

The Big Bad Wolf

The Three Little Pigs

Little Red Riding Hood

Grandma

castle

sword

dragon

princess

knight in armor

Jack and the beanstalk

GREAT STORIES

Storyland

Arthur loves to read stories.
He also likes to make up his own.
Would you like to make up a story?

giant

Goldilocks

The Three Bears

Cinderella

prince

planet

antennae

alien

spacesuit

spaceship

gingerbread house

Hansel and Gretel

witch

flag

sails

Humpty Dumpty

ship

pirate

cannons

treasure chest

Tinker Bell

Peter Pan

At the Supermarket

Arthur has to do some shopping. Can you help him find everything on his list?

juice

peaches

ice cream

banana

raspberries

pear

lime

eggplant

peas

lettuce

toilet paper

apples

soap

flour

jam

celery

MEAT

chicken

butcher

steaks

sausages

HOUSEHOLD

paper towels

BAKERY

rolls

bread

cakes

shopping cart

cereal
pineapple
eggs
paper towels
bread

cucumber

batteries

tissues

lemon

cantaloupe

dish soap

tuna fish

kiwi

garlic

beet

mustard

orange

SPECIAL

pineapples

CEREAL

bagels

muffins

DAIRY

butter

yogurt

soup

cheese

pie

milk

eggs

Swiss cheese

sauce

spaghetti

watermelon

pepper

soda

gloves

snowball

cap

hockey stick

hockey puck

valentine

thermometer

icicles

snowflakes

snow shovel

bird feeder

fire hydrant

pipe

scarf

snowman

snowsuit

boots

mitten

Winter

It's a snowy day, and
the whole world is covered in white.
But there are some bright red things that stand out.
How many can you find?

blue jay

skis

poles

ice skates

goggles

earmuffs

toboggan

birdbath gate toad mailbox tricycle roller skates eggs nest

triangle square chimney roof diamond bone circle

butterfly string fence

rain hat helmet

raincoat

galoshes bicycle training wheels

umbrella tulip crocus daffodil

robin

Spring

It is a beautiful day for flying kites and
having fun! These kites are all different shapes.
What shapes do you see?

puddle

snail rake hose trowel seeds flowerpot watering can

 fan

 ice cream truck

ice cream cone

 ice cream pop

lobster

 sandals

sunblock

Summer

A picnic at the beach is delicious on a hot summer day. The ants think so too. How many ants came to Arthur's picnic?

lighthouse

cliff

sailboat

buoy

motorboat

wave

dune

beach ball

beach bag

bathing suit

picnic basket

chips

shell

beach blanket

cup

sandwich

plate

gull

shovel

pail

sand castle

starfish

ants

 lawnmower

sunglasses

 beach umbrella

crab

pitcher

dandelion

seeds

Wampanoag Indians*

Pilgrim

turkey

moth

squirrel

acorn

wheelbarrow

branches

knife

window

leaves

tree

bush

happy   sad   surprised   pumpkin
jack-o'-lanterns

sweater

rake

Fall

D.W. is helping Arthur rake leaves.
Dad is getting ready for Halloween.
What kinds of faces did he carve?

*The Wampanoags were the Native Americans who attended the Pilgrims' first Thanksgiving.

football

gourds

witch

bat

ghost

cornstalks

mask

bull

cherries

calf

goose

tomato

wheat

hoe

milk can

At Grandpa Dave's Farm

Arthur is learning how to milk a cow. The cow has something to say about that: Moooooooo! What do some of the other animals say?

Oink-oink

Mooooooooo

pig

pigsty

cow

cowbell

fly

tail

Meow-meow

udder

pail

cat

stool

mouse

horseshoe

hay wagon

onions

watch

medicine

jellybeans

scale

shoes

French fries

television

popcorn

candy

dress

perfume

art supplies

BANK

ATM

Ice Cream Shop

escalator

CINEMA

NOW PLAYING

BIONIC BUNNY ON MARS G

PRETTY PONY, COME HOME G

TICKET BOOTH

OUT

IN

walkie-talkie

security guard

At the Shopping Mall

Arthur and D.W. agreed on a birthday present for their mom. But they can't agree on what movie to see. What movie do you think they should see?

pretzel

skirt

blouse

hair dryer

radio

soap

dice

video camera

basket

magazine

armchair

toaster

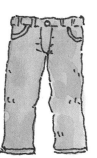
jeans

diamond ring

Bookstore

Toy Store

sundae

Jewelry

marionette

dollhouse

present

robot

bracelet

necklace   rings

greeting card

bathrobe

pay telephone

fountain

bath brush

litter can

shopping bag

tennis racket

shorts

underwear

sled   newspaper

milkshake

 train

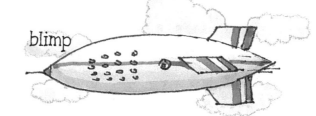 blimp

 submarine

Things That Go

What's your favorite way to get from here to there?

delivery van

Honk! Honk!

Renita's Flowers

Screech!

bicycle

RELIABLE MOVERS

Honk! Honk!

moving truck

taxi

Beep! Beep! Beep! Beep!

TAXI

Whee-eeee! Whee-eee!

police car

POLICE

Piccadilly Circus

racing car

bulldozer

jeep

oil tank truck

swimming pool

star

lantern

duffel bag

compass

cooler

thermos

sleeping bag

first-aid kit

bug repellent

firewood

Backyard Camping

Telling spooky stories around the campfire can make you imagine all sorts of strange things. What do you see in the clouds?

clouds

smoke

log

marshmallows

water bottle

fire

flashlight

raisins

fishing pole

fish

fishing net

Ping-Pong paddle

tadpole

Ping-Pong ball

hammock

tennis ball

moth

dragonfly

fly

fly swatter

owl

moon

sky

lightning bugs

fern

tent

birdhouse

hot dog

binoculars

snail

blanket

pillow

magnifying glass

raccoon

mushroom

worm

skunk

What's Inside?

Baby Kate has turned everything upside down. What a mess! Can you help Arthur and D.W. put everything back where it belongs?

toolbox

change purse

tissues

pen

keys

lipstick

comb

chewing gum

notebook

blocks

truck

teddy bear

doll

pull toy

yo-yo

lunchbox

screws

screwdriver

pliers

nails

hammer

drill

tape measure

pocketbook

toy chest

cookie

carrot sticks

juice

sandwich

apple

napkin

When Arthur Grows Up...

Here are some of the things he might be.

astronaut

fire fighter

police officer

cowboy

soldier

doctor

artist

rock star

teacher

chef

jester

construction worker

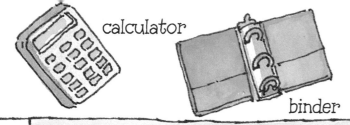 calculator

 marker

binder

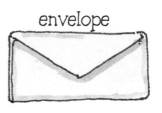 envelope

 stamp

 hole puncher

Mom at Work

Mom is an accountant. D.W. loves to visit her office. There are so many interesting things there, including a mouse that doesn't eat cheese. Can you find it?

cup

bulletin board

briefcase

lamp

pictures

TAXES

computer

telephone

important letters

drawer

desk

files

wastebasket

stapler

carpeting

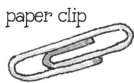 paper clip

 tape

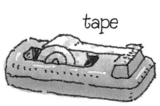 rubber bands

 pencil sharpener

 pushpin

 eraser

 thumbtack

wooden spoon

cookie cutters

birthday candles

measuring spoons

tongs

salt

pepper

timer

Dad at Work

Arthur's dad is a caterer. Sometimes Arthur helps him clean up.
He is very good at licking the spoons.

coffee

cooking oil

microwave oven

cupboard

magnets

freezer

refrigerator

dish soap

cake

sink

jam

pot

blender

mixing bowl

whisk

spatula

pastry bag

cake flour

sugar

flour

rice

dishwasher

pan

tray

colander

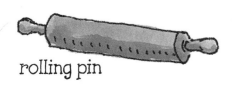

rolling pin

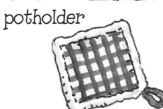

potholder

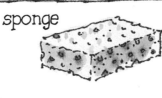

sponge

measuring cup

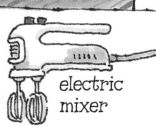

electric mixer

bench

dandelion

stream

bridge

swan

clover

pigeon

top

sweatshirt

rings

jungle gym

litter basket

At the Playground

D.W. is playing hide-and-seek and she is "it." Can you help her find Arthur, Muffy, Francine, and Binky? (Their pictures are on the last two pages.)

swings

...ready or not, here I come!

sand

sandbox

pail

grass

seesaw

pussywillow

jacks

spider

bandage

whistle

ladybug

slide

lunchbox

jump rope

lamppost

basketball hoop

bouncing ball

bell

ladder

playhouse

basketball

squirrel

caterpillar

merry-go-round

water lily

pogo stick

sidewalk

hopscotch game

sun

sand toys

trike

marbles

buttons

bottle caps

stamps

Diplodocus

Cetiosaurus

dolls

Collections

Buster has quite a collection of toy dinosaurs! People can collect all sorts of things. Do you have a collection?

marbles

pencils

caps

rocks

postcards

feathers

toy cars

coins

Stegosaurus

Triceratops

Allosaurus

shells

Tyrannosaurus rex

action figures

baseball cards

teddy bears